Year 6 English sorted — one week at a time!

This CGP book is packed with fantastic 10-Minute Workouts for regular bursts of English practice throughout Year 6.

There's one Workout for every week of the year, each covering a mixture of topics and skills. They're perfect to use as starter activities, recaps, homework tasks... and more!

We've even included a progress chart and answers to make tracking how pupils are doing that much easier.

Published by CGP

ISBN: 978 1 78908 315 6

Editors: Heather Cowley, Kelsey Hammond, Kathryn Kaiser, Hannah Roscoe, Matt Topping

With thanks to Sean Walsh and Amanda MacNaughton for the proofreading.

With thanks to Jan Greenway for the copyright research.

Contents pages © Crown Copyright, National Curriculum. Contains public sector information licensed under the Open Government Licence v3.0 - http://www.nationalarchives. gov.uk/doc/open-government-licence/version/3/

Clipart from Corel®

Printed by Elanders Ltd, Newcastle upon Tyne.

Based on the classic CGP style created by Richard Parsons.

Text, design, layout and original illustrations © Coordination Group Publications Ltd. (CGP) 2019 All rights reserved.

How to Use this Book

- This book contains <u>36 workouts</u>. We've split them into <u>3 sections</u>, one for each term, with <u>12 workouts</u> each. There's roughly one workout for <u>every week</u> of the school year.

- Each workout is out of <u>15 marks</u> and should take about <u>10 minutes</u> to complete.

- Each workout tests a variety of <u>English content</u> from the government's <u>programme of study</u>, including grammar, punctuation, spelling, comprehension and writing skills.

- The <u>first 3 workouts</u> only contain <u>up to Year 5 English content</u> — they're ideal for <u>reminding</u> students what they have learnt in <u>previous years</u>. These workouts should be done at the <u>start</u> of Year 6.

- The <u>last 9 workouts</u> only contain <u>Year 6 content</u> — they're perfect for preparing pupils for the <u>Key Stage 2 English SATS tests</u>.

- The other workouts contain a <u>mix</u> of <u>old</u> and <u>new</u> topics.

- As the book progresses, the tests increase in <u>difficulty</u>.

- <u>Answers</u> can be found at the <u>back</u> of the book.

The <u>contents page</u> will help you identify which Year 6 <u>statutory requirement</u> is being tested in each workout.

You can use these to pick the workout which best <u>suits</u> you and the needs of your class (but remember the <u>later</u> in the book, the <u>harder</u> the workout will be, so it's best to save the workouts towards the end of the book for <u>later in the year</u>).

There is a <u>tick box</u> next to each workout on the contents page. Use this to <u>record</u> which tests have been attempted. You can also use the <u>progress chart</u> to track pupils' scores.

Contents — Autumn Term

Contents — Spring Term

Contents — Summer Term

(10)

Warm up

1. Circle the correct **preposition** in the sentences below.

    I'll wait for you (after) / in I finish work.

    They might be late **before** / (because of) all the traffic.

    _____
    2 marks

2. Add one set of **brackets** to each of the sentences below.

    Rosemary (my cousin) is coming round for tea.

    I hurt my leg (the left one) when I fell down the hill.

    _____
    2 marks

3. Circle the correct spellings of the words below.

    (movement) / movemant   assistent / (assistant)

    significent / (significant)   (accident) / accidant

    _____
    2 marks

4. Tick the options where **commas** are used correctly.

    Yesterday, on my birthday, it rained all day long.   ✓

    My uncle is, my favourite relative, to go and visit.   ☐

    The lion the, leader of the pride, roared loudly.   ☐

    Alex, my youngest sister, is scared of frogs.   ✓

    _____
    2 marks

5. Add a **relative pronoun** to the sentences below.

I met a woman _____who_____ had grown ten feet tall.

My bike, _____that_____ is purple, is kept in the garage.

We have a neighbour _____who_____ mows his lawn at 6 am.

6. Rewrite this passage without the errors.

Next summer my family and I is travelling to America to see my grandparents, which I've never met. Im looking forwud to being on a plain because Jasmine, my big sister, says they're really fun. I hop we see the White House, which is wear the president lives.

Next summer my family and I are
travelling to America to see my
grandparents, who I've never met. I'm
looking forward to being on a
plane. Plane to a Jasmine, my big
sister, says they're really fun. I hope
we see the white, which is where the
president lives.

4 marks

Score:

© CGP — not to be photocopied

3

Autumn Term: Workout 1

(10)

Warm up

1. Add **commas** to the list below.

    Chris still needed to pack his swimming trunks, his
    socks, his new trainers, his book, and a pair of sunglasses. __2__

    2 marks

2. Draw lines to match each **prefix** to the correct word.

dis		flow
over		code
de		mount

    __2__

    2 marks

3. Add the missing **silent letters** to the words below.

    clim........ing   cas.........le   ....wrong

    cupboard
    cu...b....board   pa...l.....m   mus..c....le   __2-5__

    3 marks

4. Put the following adverbs in order, where 1 is the **most likely**
    to happen and 4 is the **least likely** to happen.

    [1] surely   [4] hardly   [3] perhaps   [2] probably   __2__

    2 marks

4

5. Circle the correct spellings of the words below.

My cousin has an **artificial** / **artifitial** leg.

The **inicial** / **initial** result of the review was positive.

You've been given an **official** / **offitial** warning.

3

3 marks

6. Read this passage and answer the questions.

> Erin tiptoed through the house. The wind whistled down the chimney as she crept up the stairs, successfully bypassing the creaky third step. What she couldn't see in the dark was the purring pet lying in wait on the landing, ready to pounce on the ankles of anyone foolish enough to step within reach of his razor-sharp claws...

What kind of animal do you think is waiting for Erin?

a cat

What word could the author have used instead of 'pounce'?

jump

Find and copy one word from the text which means 'avoiding'.

bypassing

3

3 marks

Score: 14·5/15

Warm up

1. Circle the missing **capital letters** in the sentences below.

   my favourite night of the week is wednesday.
   after games club, we go to gino's for pizza.

   _____
   2 marks

2. Rewrite these nouns as adjectives using the suffixes '**ful**' or '**less**'.

   fright ....

   home ....

   end ....

   hurt ....

   _____
   2 marks

3. Tick the sentences below that contain a **modal verb**.

   What do you think we should do? ☐

   We could have fish and chips for tea. ☐

   You had better take an umbrella! ☐

   They must not get caught out by the tide. ☐

   _____
   3 marks

4. Circle the correct word to complete the sentences below.

He's planning to **buy / bye** a new car.

There's a **herd / heard** of cows in that field.

5. Complete each sentence with a **relative clause**.

We want to buy a house ....

My hat, ..., was stolen.

6. Rewrite this passage so that it is in the **simple past tense**.

> Andy can't play tennis because it is winter. He asks his mum what she thinks, and she suggests an indoor sport. The next week, Andy goes to a club to learn to play squash. He comes home much happier and hugs his mum.

....

....

....

....

....

....

Score:

Warm up

1. Circle the words which should have **apostrophes**.

   Ive lost my brothers rounders bat. Can I borrow yours?

   Dianas niece is everyones favourite babysitter.

   2 marks

2. Draw lines to match each word on the left
   with its **synonym** on the right.

   | occur |
   | mischievous |
   | develop |

   | grow |
   | happen |
   | naughty |

   3 marks

3. Circle the correct spelling from each pair of words below.

   surveigh / survey   neighbour / neibour

   veyn / vein   obay / obey

   2 marks

4. Rewrite the following phrases in the **present perfect tense**.

   he eats   ....

   you feel   ....

   > Check the glossary on p.85 if you are unsure about what something means.

   2 marks

5. Complete the words with either a '**t**' or a '**c**'.

preten.........ious   deli.........ious   frac.........ious

scrump.........ious   cons.........ious   vi.........ious

_____
3 marks

6. Put **three** paragraph markers '**//**' in the passage below to show where new paragraphs should start.

> Halloween, or All Hallow's Eve, is a festival that takes place on the 31st October. Historically, it was considered by some to be the beginning of winter. There are lots of traditions associated with Halloween. One of the most famous is trick-or-treating, where children knock on people's doors and threaten to play a silly 'trick' if they don't receive a 'treat'. Other traditions include fancy-dress parties, telling scary stories and carving jack-o'-lanterns. A jack-o'-lantern is a name for a carved pumpkin with a lit candle inside. People often put them outside their houses as Halloween decorations, but the tradition began because people used to believe that jack-o'-lanterns could stop evil spirits from entering a house. To make a jack-o'-lantern, take your pumpkin and cut around the stalk to make a lid. Scoop all the flesh out of the hole you've made and carefully carve a face into the side of the pumpkin before putting a candle inside. Light the candle and replace the lid to complete your spooky jack-o'-lantern.

_____
3 marks

Score:

Autumn Term: Workout 4

1. Fill in the gap with a **noun** that comes from the verb '**excite**'.

    You could feel the .... in the air.

    _____
    1 mark

2. Add **commas** to the sentences below.

    Mr Collins whose husband works abroad is going to India.

    Nish my best friend lives in the next village.

    _____
    2 marks

3. Put a tick next to the words that are spelt incorrectly.
    Then write them out correctly on the line below.

    ☐ partial   ☐ potencial   ☐ superfitial   ☐ antisocial

    ....

    _____
    2 marks

4. Complete each sentence with an **antonym** of the word in bold.

    The sea was **rough** .... during our voyage.

    We might be **early** .... for dinner.

    The birds flew **over** .... the bridge.

    _____
    3 marks

5. Rewrite the incorrectly spelt words below.

   Please don't **interfear**.   ....

   What a **marvelus** idea!   ....

   That's not **nessessary**.   ....

3 marks

6. Rewrite the passage to make it more interesting.

   Mum had been feeling poorly. My stepdad wanted
   to cheer her up. He suggested that we bake her a
   cake. It was a strawberry cake with frosting and a
   cherry. Mum cried when we gave it to her.

   ....

   ....

   Remember to use exciting
   words to make your writing
   come to life. Try to make your
   sentences different lengths.

   ....

   ....

   ....

   ....

   ....

   ....

4 marks

Score:

11

(10)

1. Write down the **word type** that best describes the word 'present' in the sentence below.

   Wilma was asked to **present** the talent show.

   ....

   1 mark

2. Rewrite the following verbs with the suffix '**ed**'.

   defer   ....

   suffer   ....

   2 marks

3. Circle the incorrect **pronoun** in the sentence below.
   Explain why it is incorrect on the line.

   Cleo and Rocket wagged its tails when they saw us.

   ....

   3 marks

4. Add a **single dash** in the correct place in each sentence.

   Alfonso's birthday ☐ is this week ☐ he'll be 100 years old.

   The hens hid ☐ in the coop ☐ there was a fox in the bushes.

   The fog spread across the landscape ☐ it was ☐ very thick.

   3 marks

5. Rewrite these sentences in **Standard English**.

Check the glossary on p.85 if you are unsure about what something means.

I didn't get no chocolate this Easter.

....

You would of forgotten if I hadn't reminded you.

....

2 marks

6. Rewrite this passage without the errors.

Simon normally loved the beech, but today it was grey and mizerable. "Come on"! shouted simon's dad, who was paddling in the sea. "Its warmer than it looks. Simon shook his head and nelt down beside her sister to help her build a sandcastle.

....

....

....

....

....

....

4 marks

Score:

Autumn Term: Workout 6

Autumn Term: Workout 7

Warm up

1. Circle the correct spelling from each pair of words below.

   echo / ecko   ake / ache   chameleon / cameleon   _____

   1 mark

2. Fill in the gaps using the correct **prefixes** below.

   | mis | up | im | pro | dis | sub |

   ....marine   ....polite   ....honour

   ....active   ....behave   ....hill

   3 marks

3. Tick each row to show whether the clause in bold is a
   main clause or a **subordinate clause**.

	main clause	subordinate clause
Although some people dislike them, I like peas.		
I hate mushrooms because they taste slimy.		

   2 marks

4. Complete the words below using the suffix '**able**' or '**ible**'.

   avail.............   forc.............   flex.............

   valu.............   unreli.............   revers.............

   3 marks

5. Put a **colon** in the correct place in each of the lists below.

She has three favourite colours red, purple and green.

I wear extra clothes in winter a hat, a scarf and gloves. _____

2 marks

6. Read this passage and answer the questions.

She'd been planning it for weeks, and today was finally the day: Rosie was going to run away with the circus! Each night, she would dream of acrobats soaring on their trapezes, the roar of the crowds and the streaming scarlet silk of the big top. She pictured herself on the high wire with everyone watching in awe. She'd be the main spectacle, and nobody would ever have seen anything as astounding as an elephant on a tightrope.

Tick the option below that is closest in meaning to 'soaring'.

☐ cheering   ☐ flying   ☐ falling   ☐ turning

What does Rosie want to do in the circus?

....

How do you think Rosie feels in this passage?
Explain your answer.

....

....   _____

4 marks

Score: [ ]

⏱ 10

1. Add **inverted commas** to the sentences below.

    Do we need juice? asked Janine, looking at the list.

    Lucas ran over to her. Thank goodness! he gasped.

    _____
    2 marks

2. Rewrite these **verbs** with a suffix to turn them into **nouns**.

    populate   ....

    civilise   ....

    explain   ....

    _____
    3 marks

3. Circle the incorrectly spelt words below, then spell them correctly on the line.

    independence   presidant   disinfectent

    elegence   brilliant   decancy

    ....

    _____
    4 marks

4. Tick the **most formal** sentence below.

    He likes to fish, doesn't he?   ☐

    Does he like to fish?   ☐

    _____
    1 mark

5. Rewrite these two sentences as one using a **subordinating conjunction**.

Joy goes hiking. The weather is nice.

....

6. Write a short diary entry from last weekend. Use each of the **adverbials** below to link your paragraphs.

| In the morning | Later on | That night |

You don't have to write about something that's real. Use your imagination to make it as interesting as possible.

....

....

....

....

....

....

....

....

....

4 marks

Score:

Warm up

1. Rewrite the verbs in bold in the **simple past tense**.

   Anna **rides** .... her horse.

   We **catch** .... the bus at 7 o'clock.

   I **draw** .... a picture of my cat.

   <u>3 marks</u>

2. Rewrite these nouns as verbs using the suffix '**ise**'.

   fantasy ....   magnet ....

   <u>2 marks</u>

3. Tick the sentences which use **colons** correctly.

   I can't eat this as I'm allergic to: peanuts. ☐

   Alan was tired: the race was tougher than he thought. ☐

   Eric's in trouble: he's been very unkind to Danilo. ☐

   We didn't have much to eat the: seagulls stole our chips. ☐

   <u>2 marks</u>

4. Circle the word which should have an **apostrophe**.
   Rewrite the sentence adding an apostrophe in the correct place.

   The alpacas fleeces are trimmed yearly.

   ....

   <u>2 marks</u>

5. Add the missing **silent letters** to the words below.

s.........issors   ....onest   thum.........

g.........ostly   recei.........t   ....riggle

3 marks

6. Read the poem and answer the questions.

> The moon has a face like the clock in the hall;
> She shines on thieves on the garden wall,
> On streets and fields and harbour quays,
> And birdies asleep in the forks of the trees.
>
> The squalling cat and the squeaking mouse,
> The howling dog by the door of the house,
> The bat that lies in bed at noon,
> All love to be out by the light of the moon.
>
> An extract from *The Moon* by Robert Louis Stevenson

How does the poet describe the moon's face?

....

The poet describes the cat as 'squalling'.
What impression does this give you of the cat?

....

Find and copy a phrase that suggests the bat is nocturnal.

....

3 marks

Score:

Warm up

1. Circle the correct **conjunctions** in the sentences below.

   Harry was busy **when / so** I called Idris instead.

   Put some gloves on **before / because** you freeze!

   2 marks

2. Write a suitable **synonym** for each word in bold.

   This is his dream **profession**.   ....

   I never had the **chance** to tell you.   ....

   She was **eager** to win.   ....

   3 marks

3. Circle the correct spelling from each pair of words below.

   deceive / decieve   protien / protein

   reciever / receiver   seizure / siezure

   2 marks

4. Rewrite these words with a **suffix** to turn them into **nouns**.

   equip ....   repay ....

   enjoy ....   assess ....

   2 marks

5. Circle the **modal verb** in the sentence below.
   Rewrite the sentence using a more **certain** modal verb.

   We might leave the party before it ends.

   ....

2 marks

6. Read the article and answer the questions.

   Goats are four-legged farm animals that are closely related to sheep. All goats have beards and most goats also have horns (some are born without them).

   They are rumoured to eat almost anything, but their diet mainly consists of weeds and shrubs. They are also able to eat plants that are poisonous to other farm animals.

   Goats are extremely curious and nimble on their feet. They often climb trees and other obstacles. Farmers need to make sure their fences are secure, otherwise their goats will find a way to escape!

   Write an interesting heading for this article.

   ....

   Write a subheading for each of the paragraphs above:

   1: ....

   2: ....

   3: ....

4 marks

Score:

🕙 10

Warm up

1. Underline the **determiners** in the sentences below.

   Today we went to a zoo. We saw two cheeky
   orangutans and some tall giraffes. I enjoyed
   watching the crocodile while it was swimming.

   _____
   2 marks

2. Circle the correct spelling from each pair of words below.

   chef / shef   charades / sharades

   ricoshet / ricochet   moustashe / moustache

   _____
   2 marks

3. Underline the incorrectly spelt words below, then spell them
   correctly on the lines.

   The dove is a simbol of peace.   ....

   Fizical activity is good for you.   ....

   He hired a yot to sail up the coast.   ....

   _____
   3 marks

4. Circle the word which shouldn't have a **hyphen**.

   re-examine   co-operate   in-sert   co-own

   _____
   1 mark

22

5. Circle the correct word to complete the sentences below.

   We made a **prophet / profit** when we sold our house.

   After the long trek, she was extremely **weary / wary**.

   I like fresh fruit with my breakfast **cereal / serial**.

6. Rewrite this passage without the errors.

   > Daniel had an horrendous mourning: his alarm clock had run out of battry, so he underslept and woke up just five minutes before school started. He throwed on his shirt tie and trousers before thundering downstairs. "Really," muttered Miriam, you can't be late again. You're the headteecher!"

   ....

   ....

   ....

   ....

   ....

   ....

   ....

Score: [   ]

Warm up

1. Write a **possessive pronoun** which makes
    sense in each sentence below.

    That car isn't .... — we hired a red car.

    She used my comb because she'd forgotten ....

    2 marks

2. Tick the sentence which is an **exclamation**.

    How do you know he's not coming? ☐

    How cold it is outside! ☐

    Take your muddy boots off now! ☐

    1 mark

3. Spell these words correctly on the lines.

    altho ....   burugh ....

    enuff ....   breakthru ....

    4 marks

4. Circle the incorrectly spelt words below, then spell them
    correctly on the line.

    obscene   senic   adolessent   desend   scent   discern

    ....

    3 marks

5. Draw lines to match each phrase with the correct definition.

a thin, striped shirt		a shirt with thin stripes

a thin-striped shirt		a striped shirt made of thin material

1 mark

6. Rewrite the passage to make the sentences flow better.

The llamas stared at Billy. Billy walked towards their paddock. He took out the bag of food. The llamas rushed over to him. Billy offered each of them some food. The llamas gently nibbled the food in Billy's hand.

Use adverbials and conjunctions to link ideas and make the text more cohesive.

....

....

....

....

....

....

....

4 marks

Score:

1. Add an **exclamation mark** or a **full stop** to the sentences below.

    There is a tiger behind you ☐

    Tigers are a species of big cat ☐

    1 mark

2. Circle the correctly spelt words below.

    The Prime Minister is an important **politician** / **politition**.

    When crossing roads, always pay **attension** / **attention**.

    2 marks

3. Rewrite the nouns as adjectives using the **suffix** 'tial' or 'cial'.

    consequence   ....

    essence   ....

    race   ....

    3 marks

4. Underline the **adverbials** in these sentences.

    In the morning, I love to eat cornflakes.

    Penguins dance in a funny way.

    My mum keeps a secret stash of chocolate under the sink.

    3 marks

5. Change this shopping list into **bullet points**.

I need to buy balloons, one hat and a pineapple for the party.

For the party, I need to buy:

• ....

• ....

• ....

2 marks

6. Rewrite this passage so that it uses the **present tense**.

> Ameera was usually late for the train, so she hurried to the station and jumped on board. She often forgot her lunch and left it at home. Her mum sometimes drove her instead. At least she didn't have to rush on those days, unless she woke up late.

....

....

....

....

....

....

4 marks

Score:

⏱ 10

1. Add **inverted commas** to these sentences.

    Mum? Mike asked, Can you buy some biscuits?

    The ghost leapt from the cupboard and howled, Boooo!

    _____
    3 marks

2. Circle the correct spellings of the words below.

    suspicious / suspitious   uncontious / unconscious

    ambicious / ambitious   ferocious / ferotious

    _____
    2 marks

3. Circle the words that are spelt incorrectly.
    Then write them out correctly on the line below.

    plague   mosque   tonge   barbeqe   unique   leage

    ....

    _____
    3 marks

4. Tick the sentences that use verbs in the **present progressive**.

    Mia was washing the plates after dinner.   ☐

    Your dog is chasing its tail in the garden.   ☐

    Grandma will probably lose her glasses today.   ☐

    The frogs are leaping into the pond.   ☐

    _____
    2 marks

5. Add the missing **semi-colons** to this list.

In my class there is Ellie, who is great at colouring Aled, who can dance all day and David, who runs faster than anyone else.

2 marks

6. Read this recipe and then answer the questions.

> For the Cake
>
> Beat the sugar and butter together until they have a creamy texture. Add the eggs one at a time, and sift in the flour slowly. Mix to a silky consistency. Split the mixture evenly between two baking tins and bake at a low temperature for three quarters of an hour.
>
> For the Icing
>
> Whip the cream into snowy white peaks and sift in the icing sugar. Generously and vigorously spread it onto the cake once the cake has cooled.

Why do you think the recipe uses subheadings?

....

Write down the ingredients needed to make the icing.

....

Which word describes how you should put the icing on the cake?

Cautiously ☐   Sparingly ☐   Enthusiastically ☐

3 marks

Score: ☐

Warm up

1. Use **full stops** to separate the passage below into sentences.
    Circle the words which are missing **capital letters**.

    as I peered into the darkness, I could see the monster's
    eyes shining back at me it scuttled out as fast as
    lightning and I squashed it with a book i hate spiders

    _____
    2 marks

2. Complete the words with either an '**e**' or an '**a**'.

    movem.........nt   sent.........nce   disinfect.........nt

    tend.........ncy   inherit.........nce   vac.........ncy

    _____
    3 marks

3. Add **relative pronouns** to the sentences below.

    I laughed at the man .... hat had blown away.

    My mum is the one .... always makes my bed.

    Amy loved the snorkel .... she got on holiday.

    _____
    3 marks

4. Underline the **determiners** in the sentences below.

    An astronaut landed on a distant alien planet.
    Her boots crunched over the surface's jagged rocks.

    _____
    2 marks

5. Tick the sentences where the **object** is in bold.

Badgers dig **burrows**. ☐

The sun pulls the planets towards it. ☐

Magicians perform **tricks**. ☐

Alina loves trains. ☐

2 marks

6. Rewrite the passage in **Standard English**.

My grandad give me an old vase. I knew I should of keeped it safe, but instead Shane and me took it outside. It became real slippery in the rain and I couldn't get no grip on it.

There are six errors you'll need to change.

....

....

....

....

....

....

3 marks

Score: ☐

Warm up

1. Rewrite the sentences in the **simple past tense**.

   Maria loves ice cream so much that she will even have it for breakfast. Her favourite flavours are pistachio and mint.

   ....

   ....

   ....

   2 marks

2. Rewrite the following **adjectives** as **adverbs**.

   frantic   ....

   true   ....

   2 marks

3. Tick each row to show whether the noun phrase includes an **adjective** or a **preposition phrase**.

	adjective	preposition phrase
the spotty turtle		
a turtle in the pond		
some hungry turtles		
the turtle at home		

   2 marks

32

4. Circle the **adjectives** below and then use them in a sentence.

hairy   trouble   giraffe   ridiculous

....

....

3 marks

5. Add a **dash** to each sentence to separate the clauses.

I didn't have any cheese that was my first mistake.

Ralph slept all day sleeping was his favourite hobby.

2 marks

6. Rewrite the to-do list using **bullet points**.

> On Saturday, I have to wake up early, buy milk from the shop, pop into the hairdresser's and walk the dog.

On Saturday I have to:

....

....

....

....

4 marks

Score:

10

Warm up

1. Rewrite the verb in **bold** in the **past progressive**.

   The cat **chases** the puppies in the garden.

   ....

2. Add **suffixes** correctly to the words in bold to complete the sentences.

   Ravi had to give a presentation at the **confer**............

   The patients were all **transfer**............ to a different hospital.   _____

   2 marks

3. Add a **comma** to the sentence below.

   Four years ago my grandma moved to Portugal.

   Explain why the comma is needed in this sentence.

   ....

   ....   _____

   2 marks

4. Circle the correct spellings of the words below.

   exaggerate / exagerate   curiousity / curiosity

   definite / defanite   hinderance / hindrance   _____

   2 marks

5. Tick the pairs of words which are **antonyms**.

frequently / rarely ☐   unknown / familiar ☐

criticise / scold ☐   loan / lend ☐

amateur / expert ☐   disaster / calamity ☐

reveal / show ☐   foolish / rational ☐

4 marks

6. Add a **paragraph marker '//'** in the passage below to show where new a paragraph should start. Then write a **heading** for the passage and **subheadings** for each paragraph.

Lacrosse is a sport that is believed to have evolved from ball games played between Native American tribes. Traditionally, men from different tribes would compete in games which could last for days, using wooden sticks with woven nets on the end to carry the ball. Modern lacrosse is enjoyed by men and women alike in various countries across the globe. Players now use strong plastic sticks and teams consist of ten players, but the aim of the game remains the same: to score more goals than your opponents. Matches only last for about an hour — a little bit less than the original lacrosse games!

Heading: ....

Subheading 1: ....

Subheading 2: ....

4 marks

Score: ☐

Warm up

1. Add a **question mark** or **full stop** to the sentences below.

    You're going to the cinema later, aren't you ☐

    I'm not sure if you're coming with us or not ☐

    _____
    2 marks

2. Circle the correct spellings of the words below.

    The artist painted a **picture / pitcher** of the landscape.

    We have swimming lessons at the **leshure / leisure** centre.
    _____
    2 marks

3. Underline the incorrectly spelt words below, then spell them correctly on the line.

    concieve   seize   caffiene   deceive   reciept   niether

    ....
    _____
    4 marks

4. Tick the sentences which use the **passive voice**.

    My sister wrote me a letter. ☐

    The football was kicked by Rhiannon. ☐

    The fabric was stained by the ink. ☐

    Uncle Dave built the furniture. ☐

    Check the glossary on p.85 if you are unsure about what something means.

    _____
    2 marks

---

5. Explain how the different **prefixes** in the two sentences below change their meanings.

Jayden **underestimated** the height of the wall.

....

Jayden **overestimated** the height of the wall.

....

2 marks

6. Read the poem and answer the questions.

> Drops are sliding down the window pane,
> Racing along in little teams,
> Like rush hour passengers dashing for the train,
> Tiny trickles that merge into streams.
>
> They criss and cross until they pool on the sill,
> Like a mirror glinting in the light of the moon,
> Over the edge they'll eventually spill,
> Creating a mini monsoon.

Find and copy **two words** from the poem that mean 'come together'.

....

In the first verse, how can you tell the water is moving quickly?

....

3 marks

Score: [ ]

Spring Term: Workout 7

Warm up

1. Add **commas** to the list below.

   Our Christmas dinner consists of roast turkey some
   Brussels sprouts carrots and plenty of roast potatoes.

   _____
   2 marks

2. Complete each sentence with a suitable word containing '**ough**'.

   Let's play a game of .... and crosses.

   I like my .... with jam in them.

   She did a .... job of marking the tests.

   _____
   3 marks

3. Tick the sentence which uses **punctuation** correctly.

   "The forecast," declared the weatherman, "is awful." ☐

   Andrew sighed, "carrots don't give you night vision". ☐

   "How many biscuits did you eat? asked Cassie." ☐

   _____
   1 mark

4. Circle the correct spellings of the words below.

   extravagance / extravagence   buoyancy / buoyency

   incompetance / incompetence   consultancy / consultency

   significant / significent   translucant / translucent

   _____
   3 marks

5. Tick the **two** questions which are **informal**.

You are staying for tea, aren't you? ☐

Would you like to sit here? ☐

Can we practise our singing? ☐

I remembered to collect the parcel, didn't I? ☐

2 marks

6. Rewrite the passage using **adverbials** to make it more interesting and to make the sentences flow better.

> The shuttle landed on the planet's surface. Abel stared at the barren landscape. He opened the door and stepped down onto the rocky red terrain.

....

Adverbials can describe time, place and manner, so mix them up for a more interesting text.

....

....

....

....

....

....

4 marks

Score: ☐

Warm up

1. Rewrite the statement as a **question** and then as a **command**.

    Elise is going to the park.

    ....

    ....

    <u>2 marks</u>

2. Circle the correct word to complete each of the sentences below.

    Bears are much scarier **then / than** sharks.

    Micky wanted to **accept / except** the invitation.

    We don't wear shoes in **are / our** house.

    There's a large blister on my **heal / heel**.

    <u>4 marks</u>

3. Underline the **adverb of probability** in the sentences below.

    I definitely won't be having any vinegar with my dinner.

    It's a shame, but we should probably cancel the trip.

    <u>2 marks</u>

4. Underline the correct spellings of the words below.

    fascinate / fassinate   disascemble / disassemble

    disciple / dissiple   ascending / assending

    <u>2 marks</u>

5. Tick the sentence where a **semi-colon** could replace the **conjunction** in bold.

Samantha likes chocolate **but** Henry likes dog biscuits. ☐

My parrot can speak Russian **but** not very well. ☐

She opened the letter **and** began reading excitedly. ☐

1 mark

6. Read the passage and answer the questions.

SCIENTISTS MAKE AMAZING DISCOVERY

This week, scientists discovered a 100-foot-long hidden chamber inside the Great Pyramid of Giza.

New techniques were used to reveal the chamber inside the 4500-year-old pyramid.

It could be only the fourth chamber ever discovered in the pyramid, which is in the 'Valley of the Kings' area.

It's disputed as to whether any of the chambers ever served as a royal tomb.

Give two facts about the newly discovered chamber.

....

....

What type of text is the passage? Explain your answer.

....

....

4 marks

Score: ☐

Warm up

1. Circle the correct spellings of the words below.

    invasion / invation   collision / collicion

    1 mark

2. Complete the words below using '**cious**' or '**tious**'.

    ficti.............   gra.............   flirta.............

    supersti.............   suspi.............   spa.............

    3 marks

3. Use **co-ordinating conjunctions** to combine the sentences below into one sentence.

    Zain wasn't hungry. He didn't want
    his carrots. Mum said he had to eat them.

    ....

    ....

    2 marks

4. Underline the words that aren't in **Standard English** and rewrite them correctly on the line below.

    Lily were going to buy a hamster. She liked the one what her brother had bought last week. Unfortunately, the pet shop didn't have no hamsters left, so Lily got a gerbil instead.

    ....

    3 marks

5. Tick the sentences which use the **subjunctive**.

Check the glossary on p.85 if you are unsure about what something means.

He suggests talking to her teacher. ☐

If I were her, I would talk to the teacher. ☐

He suggests she talks to her teacher. ☐

He suggests that she talk to her teacher. ☐

2 marks

6. Rewrite the passage below using the **adverbials** in the boxes.

I was only going to be vegetarian for a month. I've kept going for nearly three months now. It's a lot easier than I had expected it to be. The smell of bacon sandwiches in the morning can be very tempting, but I'm holding on.

| at first | of course | rather surprisingly | in reality |

....

....

....

....

....

....

4 marks

Score: ☐

43

⏱ 10

1. Write a sentence below using the verb '**sleep**' in the **present progressive**.

   ....

   1 mark

2. Underline the **adverbials** in the passage below.

   Over the last five days, they'd sailed across a ferocious ocean.

   The mighty waves had more or less destroyed their boat.

   They knew they had to find the island before the sun set.

   3 marks

3. Circle the correct spellings of the words below.

   despicable / despicible   recognisably / recognisibly

   tangible / tangable   inaudably / inaudibly

   2 marks

4. Use the definitions below to find the missing words
   with '**ou**' in them. Write the words on the lines.

   of a small age   ....

   twice as many   ....

   one of the five senses ....

   3 marks

5. Replace each of the words in **bold** with a more **informal** word.

The beef was **superb**, but the gravy was **unsatisfactory**.

....

....

2 marks

6. Rewrite the passage to make it more **interesting**.

The T-Rex entered the forest, chasing the triceratops. Its feet made a loud noise as they hit the ground. This made the trees shake. It opened its mouth to let out a roar.

....

....

....

....

....

....

....

4 marks

Score:

10

Warm up

1. Rewrite the sentence below using the **present perfect** form.

    My grandad and I visited Cornwall.

    ....

2. Underline the words that are spelt **incorrectly**
    and rewrite them correctly on the line.

    invisible   sustainible   infallably   honourably

    ....

    2 marks

3. Rewrite these nouns with a **suffix** to turn them into **adjectives**.

    function   ....

    deceit   ....

    defence   ....

    master   ....

    2 marks

4. Add the missing **punctuation** to the passage below.

    Cora had lost her two cats bowls. " Where could they be "

    she wailed. " It's fine " said Ted " they're in the sink! "

    2 marks

5. Circle the **colons** used **incorrectly** in the passage below.

Sadly,: my pizza burnt: I forgot to set the oven: timer. It
wasn't very nice: it was a bit black: and crispy. I'll remember
the timer: next week: I won't make that mistake again.

6. Rewrite this passage without the errors.

When I were growing up, I dreamed of becomming a
volcanologist (a scientist which studies volcanoes). I
used to watch volcano documentaries on are TV and
thought they are so exciting! I'd love to see Mt. Etna,
who is one the of the worlds' most active volcanoes.

....

....

....

....

....

....

....

4 marks

Score:

47

Warm up

1. Circle the correct spellings of the words below.

    pyramid / piramid   tyresome / tiresome

    mistery / mystery   symphony / simphony

    _____
    2 marks

2. Underline the words which need a **hyphen** below,
    then write them correctly on the line.

    coownership   halfway   reignite

    selfhelp   rosetinted   extraordinary

    ....
    _____
    3 marks

3. Circle the incorrect **apostrophe** in the sentence below.
    Explain why it is incorrect on the line.

    This isn't the boys' meal — it's Kim's.

    ....
    _____
    2 marks

4. Circle all the **suffixes** which can be added to each word below.

equal	ise	ful	ity
fix	able	ation	ous
mess	ily	ify	age

    _____
    3 marks

5. Underline the **active** sentences in the passage.

The mouse was chased across the room by the cat. The cat
pounced and the mouse quickly squeezed itself under the door.
The cat hit the door hard. Its nose was bruised in the collision. _____

2 marks

6. Rewrite the passage so that its ideas are **linked** between paragraphs.

Many animals are nocturnal, meaning they're active at night.

Owls use their eyesight and hearing to hunt in the dark.
Their wings glide silently so they can avoid detection.

When day breaks, they return to their roosts,
which is why they're rarely seen by people.

You can repeat a word
or phrase to link ideas
between paragraphs.

....

....

....

....

....

....

....

3 marks

Score: [   ]

Warm up

1. Underline the **subordinating conjunctions** in the passage below.

I can't wait to use my new toaster when it arrives. It looks very fancy, although I don't know how it actually works. I hope I like it because it was quite expensive.

3 marks

2. Circle the correct spelling from each pair of words below.

    thoroughfare / thorughfare   toughest / taughest

    fought / fourt   plaughing / ploughing

2 marks

3. Add **commas** to these sentences to make their meaning clearer.

    After they finished cooking Bob Sue and Rik watched TV.

    When we were painting Tom Leila and I listened to music.

    Before they met Fiona Jamal and Lin were best friends.

3 marks

4. Underline the sentences that contain a **subjunctive form**.

    The match was nearly over. Abby demanded that Sophie pass her the ball. She was the best player, and she ran so fast. Sometimes, it looked as if she were flying.

2 marks

5. Write down two words that belong to the same **word family** as the words below.

before   forearm   unforeseen

....

2 marks

6. Read the passage and answer the questions.

Earthquakes occur at plate boundaries, where the pieces of the Earth's crust meet. At some plate boundaries, these pieces are grinding against each other. Sometimes, they get stuck, which causes pressure to build up. When this pressure is released, it causes an earthquake.

The largest earthquake ever recorded was the Great Chilean Earthquake of 1960. It caused considerable damage, destroying several towns and creating tidal waves which travelled across the Pacific Ocean to Japan.

What does the word 'grinding' mean in the passage?

....

What does the word 'considerable' tell you about the damage?

....

Give one consequence of the Great Chilean Earthquake.

....

3 marks

Score:

⏱ 10

1. Rewrite the sentences below in the **past tense**.

    Viv keeps hens in her garden. In winter, she
    brings them in because their feathers freeze.

    ....

    ....

    3 marks

2. Add the **silent** letters to the words below.

    resi..........ned   ....nuckle

    cres..........ent   autum..........

    2 marks

3. Underline the **relative clauses** in the passage below.

    > Check the glossary on p.85 if you are unsure about what something means.

    Kat went to buy new shoes, which was very

    problematic. She was one of those rare people

    who had one foot bigger than the other.

    2 marks

4. Circle the correct spelling in each pair of words below.

    industryous / industrious   prestigious / prestigeous

    simultanious / simultaneous   harmonious / harmoneous

    2 marks

5. Add **colons** to the passage below.

I've always wanted a sloth as a pet I think they're
so cute and cuddly. I doubt they would like living in
Cumbria they are used to tropical weather.

2 marks

6. Rewrite this passage without the errors.

Fran and Joe were playing golf on there holidays. They'd
got to the twelfth hole when a wasp flies into Joe's shirt. He
yelped "Get it out!" Fran had took a newspaper from her
bag and began to swot Joe's shirt. Everyone watched Fran;
as she chased Joe with the newspaper. How embarassing!

....

....

....

....

....

....

4 marks

Score:

(10)

Warm up

1. Rewrite the sentence, changing the **prefix** of the word in bold so that the sentence means the **opposite**.

   I **uploaded** the photos last night.

   ....

   1 mark

2. Complete the passage below with the **past progressive form** of the verbs in bold.

   Pat and Pam **argue** .... about what was

   for tea. I **laugh** .... at them.

   2 marks

3. Circle the correct word to complete each sentence below.

   My birthday is the **forth / fourth** of November.

   I fastened the horse's **bridal / bridle**.

   It was very tough to **real / reel** in the giant fish.

   You have to **knead / need** the dough vigorously.

   4 marks

4. Circle the correct spellings of the words below.

   controversy / controversey   privilege / privilige

   stomack / stomach   forty / fourty

   2 marks

5. Add **commas** to the sentences below for **parenthesis**.

Sam bought the smallest kitten the one with the stripes after lots of debating. He thought that his other cat a tabby called Charlie needed some company.

6. Rewrite the passage to make it flow better.

> Alick was a writer (specifically a writer of poetry). His most famous poem, which was called 'All Out', was published in a book. He took inspiration from cricket (his favourite sport was cricket). Another book he wrote was a book about mountaineering with his friend, who was a famous mountaineer.

Removing any unnecessary words or phrases will help the text to flow better.

....

....

....

....

....

....

....

....

Score:

1. Circle the correct spellings of the words below.

    decietfully / deceitfully   conceited / concieted

    _____
    1 mark

2. Circle the correct word to complete each sentence below.

    I have my **initials / inicials** on my hockey uniform.

    Kit has brilliant **spatial / spachial** awareness.

    I saw it advertised in a **commertial / commercial**.

    I live in a quiet **residential / residencial** area.

    _____
    2 marks

3. Underline the **subject** of each of the sentences below.

    The referee blows the whistle.

    At midnight, the boat was hit by a tidal wave.

    Hashmina dives with sharks.

    _____
    3 marks

4. Rewrite the question below in a more **formal** way.

    Foxes are nocturnal animals, aren't they?

    ....

    _____
    1 mark

5. Circle all the words below that are **antonyms** of 'moving'.

unemotional   fixed   transporting

remaining   motionless   dynamic

leaving   immobile   tense

4 marks

6. Rewrite the passage below as a table.

Flight Departure Information

The lunchtime flight to Rome (originally at 12:17) is delayed and will depart at 12:27. The afternoon flight to Shanghai, scheduled for 15:30, is delayed by 15 minutes, so will now depart at 15:45. The 19:55 flight to Oslo is on time, as is the 23:09 flight set to depart to Miami.

Destination	Time of Departure

4 marks

Score:

Summer Term: Workout 5

1. Write a suitable **synonym** for the words below on the lines.

    adventurous   ....

    punctual   ....

    2 marks

2. Complete the **bold** words below with '**tious**' or '**cious**'.

    My brother never does the washing-up. He's very

    tena............... in refusing to do it. I think he needs

    to change his **atro**............... attitude.

    2 marks

3. Complete the sentences below using a group of **homophones**.

    After our walk, my dog had very muddy ....·

    Can you please .... the video?

    Mum looks very nervous when dad .... the tea.

    3 marks

4. Circle the more **formal** word in each of the pairs below.

    scribble / note   ominous / spooky

    communicative / chatty   nasty / vile

    2 marks

Summer Term: Workout 5   © CGP — not to be photocopied

58

5. Rewrite the sentences below in the **active** voice.

My garden was completely ruined by the squirrels.

My flowers were demolished by the pesky critters!

....

....

2 marks

6. Rewrite the passage using more **formal** language.

Polar bears are proper interesting animals. They're
the largest type of bear and can weigh more
than several men. Their fur is actually clear,
but tons of people reckon it's white. They can go
for many months without munching on anything.

....

....

....

....

....

....

4 marks

Score:

59

Summer Term: Workout 6

Warm up

1. Add a **hyphen** to the sentence below to show that Ibrahim's tea was very hot.

    Ibrahim poured himself a cup of red hot tea.

    _____
1 mark

2. Circle the correct spellings of the words below.

    urgency / urgancy   turbulence / turbulance

    vacency / vacancy   observant / observent

    substence / substance   transparancy / transparency

    _____
3 marks

3. Circle the incorrect **semi-colons** in the text below.

    Lena loves unusual sports like; octopush, which is
    underwater hockey; bog snorkelling, which is very
    messy; and; water polo, which is very competitive!

    _____
2 marks

4. Underline the words that are spelt incorrectly.
    Write them correctly underneath.

    interference   transferrence   suffered

    deferal   differing   referreeing

    ....

    _____
3 marks

60

5. Add **colons** to the sentences below.

Washing a dog is quite simple wet its fur, apply shampoo, rinse with water and run away fast.

There are lots of tasty herbs to use with chicken thyme, parsley, coriander and sage.

6. Write an interesting passage about a school trip you remember. Use each of the **adverbials** below to link your paragraphs.

| in addition | as a consequence | last of all |

....

....

....

....

....

....

....

....

4 marks

Score:

61

10

Warm up

1. Tick the sentence which uses a **semi-colon** correctly.

    I went to bed really late; I'm exhausted today. ☐

    Azra can't have a hamster; because she's allergic to them. ☐

    _____
    1 mark

2. Complete the **bold** words below with '**ible**', '**ably**' or '**ibly**'.

    I'll have a pie — **prefer**.............. a cheese and onion one.

    These cupcakes are **irresist**.............. good.

    My dad's new car is a **convert**...............

    _____
    3 marks

3. Circle the correct spellings of the words below.

    I was **chuffed / choughed** to win first prize.

    My scooter stunt was lacking in **forethort / forethought**.

    I love to bake **sourdow / sourdough** bread.

    _____
    3 marks

4. Underline the correct spellings of the words below.

    restaurant / restuarant   equipment / equiptment

    category / catagory   nuissance / nuisance

    _____
    2 marks

5. Rewrite the sentence below in the **passive** voice.

Check the glossary on p.85 if you are unsure about what something means.

Jerry dropped the birthday cake.

....

2 marks

6. Read the poem and answer the questions.

Across the lonely beach we flit,
One little sandpiper and I,
And fast I gather, bit by bit,
The scattered driftwood, bleached and dry.
The wild waves reach their hands for it,
The wild wind raves, the tide runs high,
As up and down the beach we flit,
One little sandpiper and I.

An extract from *The Sandpiper* by Celia Thaxter

What does the word 'flit' suggest about how the sandpiper moves?

....

How do you know that the beach is isolated?

....

Write down two things that you are told about the driftwood.

....

....

4 marks

Score: [ ]

63

Warm up

1. Add 'able', 'ible', 'ably' or 'ibly' to complete the sentences.

    Joanna has always been a **like**.......... person. She is

    unbeliev.......... clever, but her behaviour in class is simply

    impermiss........... She needs to behave more **respons**............

    2 marks

2. Circle the correct word to complete each sentence below.

    I like crisps more **then / than** sweets or chocolate.

    He paid me a lovely **complement / compliment**.

    The changes will come into **effect / affect** next year.

    3 marks

3. Add a **colon** in the correct place in each sentence.

    I didn't eat the cupcakes I was upstairs watching TV.

    You shouldn't accept his apology he doesn't mean it.

    2 marks

4. Underline the incorrectly spelt words below, then spell them
    correctly on the line.

    embarass   prejudice   queue   secretery

    ....

    2 marks

5. Put a tick in each row to show whether each sentence
    is in the **active voice** or the **passive voice**.

	active	passive
The dog jumped into the lake.		
The runner tripped by the finish line.		
The cake must be finished by tomorrow.		
Mandy was delighted by the news.		

2 marks

6. Rewrite the passage below using **bullet points**.

> There are four steps to making a dreamcatcher. First,
> cut a hollow circle out of card. Next, stretch colourful
> string across the circle. Add feathers and beads for
> decoration. Finally, attach a loop of string to hang it.

....

....

....

....

....

....

4 marks

Score: [   ]

Summer Term: Workout 9

Warm up

1. Rewrite the sentence below in the **passive** voice.

   John fixed the old front gate.

   ....

   1 mark

2. Underline the correct spellings of the words below.

   preconceived / preconcieved   decievingly / deceivingly

   reciever / receiver   perceive / percieve

   _____
   2 marks

3. Add the **silent letters** to the words below.

   Harry's head was **nes**..........**led** amongst the pillows.

   I was **assi**..........**ned** the role of scribe for our task.

   Finn was **dou**..........**tful** he would score a goal.

   _____
   3 marks

4. Complete the words in **bold** with 'ence' or 'ance'.

   Jameela and her sister Janine are runners with incredible

   endur............. They've won many races thanks to their

   persist............ and determination. Their **resembl**.............

   is so strong that they often get mistaken for one another.

   _____
   3 marks

5. Circle the incorrect **semi-colons** in the text below.

I bought my sister a game; it looks like it'll be fun.
I'm usually terrible at games; so I'll probably lose. My
sister is only really good at games; because she cheats! _____

2 marks

6. Put **two** paragraph markers '**//**' in the passage below to show
    where new paragraphs should start. Write a heading for
    each paragraph on the lines.

In previous centuries, foreign travel for people in the UK
was almost entirely limited to Europe. They were able to
cross the English Channel using boats and could then travel
around the continent using horse-drawn carriages or steam
locomotives. Only the richest members of society could afford
to make these trips. Following the development of the steam
engine, steamships were brought into operation. These were
large ships which could carry thousands of passengers across
the Atlantic Ocean to America. The journey was incredibly
slow, expensive and sometimes dangerous. Nowadays, most
people use aeroplanes to travel from the UK to America. This
became popular from the middle of the 20th century, with
the journey time being significantly shorter. Over time,
flying has also become much cheaper, allowing many
more people to travel across the Atlantic Ocean.

1: ....

2: ....

3: ....

4 marks

Score: [   ]

Warm up

1. Add '**t**' or '**c**' to the words below.

   confiden..........ial   sequen..........ial

   sacrifi..........ial   finan..........ial

2. Add '**ou**' or '**au**' to the words below.

   I cleaned the kitchen **thor**..........**ghly**.

   The clown's juggling was **l**..........**ghable**.

   The test was **t**..........**gher** than Milly expected.

   We were all **distr**..........**ght** after our defeat.

3. Rewrite the sentences below using more **formal** vocabulary.

   It's getting late, so I'm going to head off now.

   ....

   Our meal last night was rubbish.

   ....

   The kitchen is messy; look at the mucky plates.

   ....

68

4. Circle the words that need a **hyphen**.

    I had a supersized pie as a midmorning snack. It was
    delicious! I have no selfcontrol when it comes to food. _____
                                                          2 marks

5. Circle the **subjects** and underline the **objects** in the
    sentences below.

    Hannah's stepsister bought three scarves.

    The robot bumped into Edmund. _____
                                   2 marks

6. Rewrite the passage to make it more **interesting**.

    Alice's cooking was bad. She had burned the potatoes.
    The fire alarm was going off and the kitchen was full of
    smoke. She stopped cooking and went out for a pizza.

    ....

    ....

    ....

    ....

    ....
                                                          4 marks

    Score:

(10)

Warm up

1. Tick the pairs of words which are **antonyms**.

    significant / trivial ☐   enraged / irate ☐

    miniscule / microscopic ☐   absurd / rational ☐

    2 marks

2. Circle all the **silent letters** in the words below.

    d e b r i s   j e o p a r d y   a i s l e

    s u b t l y   w h i s t l e   a s t h m a

    3 marks

3. Complete the **bold** words below with '**tious**' or '**cious**'.

    viva..............   overcau..............

    judi..............   mali..............

    2 marks

4. Add **dashes** to the passage below.

    Zebras evolved stripes for camouflage they help
    them to avoid predators. When zebras are moving
    in a herd, their stripes act as an optical illusion they
    conceal individual zebras. Not all zebras are black and
    white some species can have brown stripes.

    3 marks

5. Add a **hyphen** to each sentence to make its meaning clearer.

I've never tried a deep fried chocolate bar.

Liam is running a cross country race tomorrow.

6. Read the passage and answer the questions.

> Poison dart frogs are native to tropical rainforests.
> They are so named because tribes use them to poison
> hunting darts. What they lack in size (they can be as
> small as 20 mm), they make up for in potency, as a
> single frog's poison can kill several full-grown men.
>
> Mysteriously, captive poison dart frogs aren't poisonous
> at all. This means that they must get their poison
> from something in their natural habitat. What
> that something is has eluded biologists so far.

Where does this creature's name originate from?

....

What do you think the phrase 'they make up for' means?

....

What does the phrase 'eluded biologists so far' suggest?

....

....

3 marks

Score:

⏱ 10

Warm up

1. Circle the **silent** letters in the words below.

    m o r t g a g e   s p a g h e t t i

    a c q u i r e   b a l l e t

    2 marks

2. Add **suffixes** correctly to the words in
    bold to complete the sentences.

    The judges are **confer**............ about their decision.

    From the hefty price, I **infer**............ that they would be good.

    2 marks

3. Tick the **informal** sentences below.

    My alarm clock just won't stop going off.   ☐

    If I were to choose a colour, it would be blue.   ☐

    Giorgio is rather grumpy this morning, isn't he?   ☐

    Philippa was a sophisticated woman.   ☐

    2 marks

4. Underline the **object** of each sentence below.

    The factory's chimneys were puffing out thick grey smoke.

    The heavy frost had attacked the plants.

    2 marks

72

5. Underline the clauses that contain a **subjunctive form**.

If I were the headmaster, I'd put trampolines in every room.

I'd demand exams be stopped and I'd abolish school uniforms.

I'd also request that our maths teacher wear a clown nose.

3 marks

6. Rewrite the passage so that its ideas are **linked** between paragraphs.

At the end of my lane is an old sweetshop. It has tiny shuttered windows and a thatched roof.

Its shelves groan under the weight of the heavy glass jars filled with every kind of sweet imaginable.

As soon as I get my pocket money, I run there as fast as I can to buy mint humbugs.

You can use a repeated word or phrase to link ideas between paragraphs.

....

....

....

....

....

....

....

4 marks

Score:

Progress Chart

Fill in the progress chart after you finish each workout.

Put your scores in here to see how you've done.
Each workout is out of 15 marks.

	Autumn Term	Spring Term	Summer Term
Workout 1			
Workout 2			
Workout 3			
Workout 4			
Workout 5			
Workout 6			
Workout 7			
Workout 8			
Workout 9			
Workout 10			
Workout 11			
Workout 12			